CONTENTS

POKéMON™
ANNUAL 2007

Pedigree®

Published by Pedigree Books Limited
Beech Hill House, Walnut Gardens, Exeter, Devon EX4 4DH.
E-mail: books@pedigreegroup.co.uk

Published 2006

£7.99

Meet the Characters!

ASH

Ash is headstrong, impulsive and often overconfident, but with good reason. He has developed into one of the best Trainers in the world of Pokémon. He finished in the top 16 in the Indigo League, beat the Orange League and made the semi-finals of the Johto League. However, Ash is still learning!

Ash has a good relationship with his Pokémon, preferring to treat them as friends than as pets. Many of his Pokémon chose to follow him, instead of being caught by him in battle!

PIKACHU

Pikachu is Ash's best friend – his first and most powerful Pokémon. Pikachu isn't usually a starter Pokémon, but Ash overslept on the morning he was supposed to start his journey and, when he got there, Pikachu was the only Pokémon left. When Ash made his journey to the far-off Hoenn region, Pikachu was the only Pokémon he chose to take with him.

MAY

May has just started her Pokémon journey and she has a lot to live up to – her father is the Petalburg City Gym Leader, Norman. May has decided not to enter badge battles. Instead, she enters her Pokémon in Contests, where they are judged on the beauty rather than the power of their attacks.

BROCK

Brock is the oldest of the friends and he used to be the Pewter City Gym Leader. He's a great cook who loves to feed his friends. His greatest ambition is to be a Pokémon breeder.

TEAM MAGMA

Team Magma is a gang that loves land-based Pokémon. They want to create more places for these Pokémon to live by making more land space. They have even tried to blow up a volcano to create more land! Luckily, Ash and his friends foiled their plans.

TEAM AQUA

Team Aqua is a dangerous gang that loves Water-type Pokémon. They'd like to give those Pokémon more places to live by increasing the size of the oceans. To do this, they want to find the legendary Pokémon Kyogre, which has the ability to create torrential rain.

TEAM ROCKET

Jessie, James and Meowth make up Team Rocket. They steal Pokémon, conduct wicked experiments to make them more powerful and don't care what laws they break. Luckily, they aren't very good at it!

MAX

Max is May's younger brother, and knows far more about Pokémon than most experienced Trainers do! He isn't old enough to train Pokémon yet and he admires Ash very much. But Max's greatest hero is his father, Norman.

1 BULBASAUR
TYPE: Grass/Poison
ABILITY: Overgrow

2 IVYSAUR
TYPE: Grass/Poison
ABILITY: Overgrow

3 VENUSAUR
TYPE: Grass/Poison
ABILITY: Overgrow

4 CHARMANDER
TYPE: Fire
ABILITY: Blaze

5 CHARMELEON
TYPE: Fire
ABILITY: Blaze

6 CHARIZARD
TYPE: Fire/Flying
ABILITY: Blaze

7 SQUIRTLE
TYPE: Water
ABILITY: Torrent

8 WARTORTLE
TYPE: Water
ABILITY: Torrent

9 BLASTOISE
TYPE: Water
ABILITY: Torrent

10 CATERPIE
TYPE: Bug
ABILITY: Shield Dust

11 METAPOD
TYPE: Bug
ABILITY: Shed Skin

12 BUTTERFREE
TYPE: Bug/Flying
ABILITY: Compoundeyes

13 WEEDLE
TYPE: Bug/Poison
ABILITY: Shield Dust

14 KAKUNA
TYPE: Bug/Poison
ABILITY: Shed Skin

15 BEEDRILL
TYPE: Bug/Poison
ABILITY: Swarm

16 PIDGEY
TYPE: Normal/Flying
ABILITY: Keen Eye

17 PIDGEOTTO
TYPE: Normal/Flying
ABILITY: Keen Eye

18 PIDGEOT
TYPE: Normal/Flying
ABILITY: Keen Eye

19 RATTATA
TYPE: Normal
ABILITY: Run Away/Guts

20 RATICATE
TYPE: Normal
ABILITY: Run Away/Guts

21 SPEAROW
TYPE: Normal/Flying
ABILITY: Keen Eye

22 FEAROW
TYPE: Normal/Flying
ABILITY: Keen Eye

23 EKANS
TYPE: Poison
ABILITY: Intimidate/Shed Skin

24 ARBOK
TYPE: Poison
ABILITY: Intimidate/Shed Skin

25 PIKACHU
TYPE: Electric
ABILITY: Static

26 RAICHU
TYPE: Electric
ABILITY: Static

27 SANDSHREW
TYPE: Ground
ABILITY: Sand Veil

28 SANDSLASH
TYPE: Ground
ABILITY: Sand Veil

29 NIDORAN♀
TYPE: Poison
ABILITY: Poison Point

30 NIDORINA
TYPE: Poison
ABILITY: Poison Point

31 NIDOQUEEN
TYPE: Poison/Ground
ABILITY: Poison Point

32 NIDORAN♂
TYPE: Poison
ABILITY: Poison Point

33 NIDORINO
TYPE: Poison
ABILITY: Poison Point

34 NIDOKING
TYPE: Poison/Ground
ABILITY: Poison Point

35 CLEFAIRY
TYPE: Normal
ABILITY: Cute Charm

36 CLEFABLE
TYPE: Normal
ABILITY: Cute Charm

37 VULPIX
TYPE: Fire
ABILITY: Flash Fire

38 NINETALES
TYPE: Fire
ABILITY: Flash Fire

39 JIGGLYPUFF
TYPE: Normal
ABILITY: Cute Charm

40 WIGGLYTUFF
TYPE: Normal
ABILITY: Cute Charm

41 ZUBAT
TYPE: Poison/Flying
ABILITY: Inner Focus

42 GOLBAT
TYPE: Poison/Flying
ABILITY: Inner Focus

43 ODDISH
TYPE: Grass/Poison
ABILITY: Chlorophyll

44 GLOOM
TYPE: Grass/Poison
ABILITY: Chlorophyll

45 VILEPLUME
TYPE: Grass/Poison
ABILITY: Chlorophyll

46 PARAS
TYPE: Bug/Grass
ABILITY: Effect Spore

47 PARASECT
TYPE: Bug/Grass
ABILITY: Effect Spore

48 VENONAT
TYPE: Bug/Poison
ABILITY: Compoundeyes

49 VENOMOTH
TYPE: Bug/Poison
ABILITY: Shield Dust

50 DIGLETT
TYPE: Ground
ABILITY: Sand Veil/Arena Trap

51 DUGTRIO
TYPE: Ground
ABILITY: Sand Veil/Arena Trap

52 MEOWTH
TYPE: Normal
ABILITY: Pickup

53 PERSIAN
TYPE: Normal
ABILITY: Limber

54 PSYDUCK
TYPE: Water
ABILITY: Damp/Cloud Nine

55 GOLDUCK
TYPE: Water
ABILITY: Damp/Cloud Nine

56 MANKEY
TYPE: Fighting
ABILITY: Vital Spirit

57 PRIMEAPE
TYPE: Fighting
ABILITY: Vital Spirit

58 GROWLITHE
TYPE: Fire
ABILITY: Intimidate/Flash Fire

59 ARCANINE
TYPE: Fire
ABILITY: Intimidate/Flash Fire

60 POLIWAG
TYPE: Water
ABILITY: Water Absorb/Damp

61 POLIWHIRL
TYPE: Water
ABILITY: Water Absorb/Damp

62 POLIWRATH
TYPE: Water/Fighting
ABILITY: Water Absorb/Damp

63 ABRA
TYPE: Psychic
ABILITY: Synchronize/Inner Focus

64 KADABRA
TYPE: Psychic
ABILITY: Synchronize/Inner Focus

65 ALAKAZAM
TYPE: Psychic
ABILITY: Synchronize/Inner Focus

66 MACHOP
TYPE: Fighting
ABILITY: Guts

67 MACHOKE
TYPE: Fighting
ABILITY: Guts

68 MACHAMP
TYPE: Fighting
ABILITY: Guts

69 BELLSPROUT
TYPE: Grass/Poison
ABILITY: Chlorophyll

70 WEEPINBELL
TYPE: Grass/Poison
ABILITY: Chlorophyll

71 VICTREEBEL
TYPE: Grass/Poison
ABILITY: Chlorophyll

72 TENTACOOL
TYPE: Water/Poison
ABILITY: Clear Body/Liquid Ooze

73 TENTACRUEL
TYPE: Water/Poison
ABILITY: Clear Body/Liquid Ooze

74 GEODUDE
TYPE: Rock/Ground
ABILITY: Rock Head/Sturdy

75 GRAVELER
TYPE: Rock/Ground
ABILITY: Rock Head/Sturdy

76 GOLEM
TYPE: Rock/Ground
ABILITY: Rock Head/Sturdy

77 PONYTA
TYPE: Fire
ABILITY: Run Away/Flash Fire

78 RAPIDASH
TYPE: Fire
ABILITY: Run Away/Flash Fire

79 SLOWPOKE
TYPE: Water/Psychic
ABILITY: Oblivious/Own Tempo

80 SLOWBRO
TYPE: Water/Psychic
ABILITY: Oblivious/Own Tempo

81 MAGNEMITE
TYPE: Electric/Steel
ABILITY: Magnet Pull/Sturdy

82 MAGNETON
TYPE: Electric/Steel
ABILITY: Magnet Pull/Sturdy

83 FARFETCH'D
TYPE: Normal/Flying
ABILITY: Keen Eye/Inner Focus

84 DODUO
TYPE: Normal/Flying
ABILITY: Run Away/Early Bird

85 DODRIO
TYPE: Normal/Flying
ABILITY: Run Away/Early Bird

86 SEEL
TYPE: Water
ABILITY: Thick Fat

87 DEWGONG
TYPE: Water/Ice
ABILITY: Thick Fat

88 GRIMER
TYPE: Poison
ABILITY: Stench/Sticky Hold

89 MUK
TYPE: Poison
ABILITY: Stench/Sticky Hold

90 SHELLDER
TYPE: Water
ABILITY: Shell Armour

91 CLOYSTER
TYPE: Water/Ice
ABILITY: Shell Armour

92 GASTLY
TYPE: Ghost/Poison
ABILITY: Levitate

93 HAUNTER
TYPE: Ghost/Poison
ABILITY: Levitate

94 GENGAR
TYPE: Ghost/Poison
ABILITY: Levitate

95 ONIX
TYPE: Rock/Ground
ABILITY: Rock Head/Sturdy

96 DROWZEE
TYPE: Psychic
ABILITY: Insomnia

Part 1 ARE YOU A POKÉMON MASTER?

Training to become a Pokémon Master is not an easy task. There are many challenges to face and battles to engage. But with a true heart and a brave spirit, you will always have a chance! Stay calm and answer these questions to discover your destiny!

1. What does this Pokémon evolve into?
A. Ivysaur ☐
B. Seadra ☐
C. Goldeen ☐

2. What type of Pokémon is Torchic?
A. Electric ☐
B. Fire ☐
C. Water ☐

3. What category of Pokémon is Skitty?
A. Flower ☐
B. Magnet ☐
C. Kitten ☐

4. What are Rattata's abilities?

    A. Run Away and Guts ☐
    B. Intimidate and Run Away ☐
    C. Guts and Shed Skin ☐

5. How heavy is Groudon in kilograms?

    A. 750 ☐
    B. 950 ☐
    C. 600 ☐

6. Which is the only Pokémon to carry a leaf in its mouth?

    A. Magmar ☐
    B. Starmie ☐
    C. Ash's Treecko ☐

Now check your answers. Each correct answer earns one point. Keep a note of your score – your test will continue later!

DRAW YOUR OWN PIKACHU

Use these grids to draw your own Pikachu. Copy the grid and practise as many times as you like. When you can draw Pikachu, practise drawing Ash. Remember to use a pencil so you can rub mistakes out! Then grab your sketchbook and try illustrating your own Pokémon adventure!

GIANT FIRE-TYPE WORDSEARCH

Can you find the names of these fire-type Pokémon in the wordsearch?
(Hint – the words may be upside down or diagonal as well as left to right or right to left!)

S	U	D	W	D	H	F	P	Y	T	H	A	R	A	T
K	F	H	V	X	E	Y	S	J	P	O	E	G	S	V
P	S	E	R	T	L	O	M	N	I	D	R	P	H	E
O	P	U	J	Y	F	E	A	D	N	I	L	H	S	W
A	N	C	F	J	S	U	K	A	T	E	Q	D	A	A
K	E	H	D	F	E	I	M	B	J	R	H	O	D	R
J	C	N	I	Y	L	R	O	T	L	G	X	A	I	O
W	N	Q	B	L	A	Z	I	K	E	N	I	F	P	K
A	O	S	S	H	T	S	R	H	K	D	P	H	A	L
S	E	A	C	R	E	Y	W	A	T	G	L	J	R	I
L	R	G	F	V	N	A	V	A	L	I	U	Q	D	A
U	A	W	P	U	I	C	B	T	R	K	V	S	F	L
G	L	A	U	R	N	V	L	F	S	Y	T	I	O	P
M	F	I	S	J	T	I	O	X	P	O	N	Y	T	A
A	Z	R	Q	K	M	C	S	R	E	B	I	U	T	B

Blaziken
Vulpix
Ninetales

Charmander
Ponyta
Flareon
Moltres

Slugma
Rapidash
Quilava

15

CLAMPERL OF WISDOM

Ash and his friends were on their way to Mossdeep City. They had decided to take the ferry and enjoy a little island hopping on the way.

"Maisie Island coming up!" Brock grinned.

"Cool!" said Max." I hope we get to see some rare Pokémon!"

Suddenly Pikachu gave a cry. A Spoink was in the middle of the sea, floating on a log.

"How did it end up way out here?" gasped Ash.

As they watched, a huge wave knocked it off the log.

"Captain, stop the ship!" Ash ordered. "Hold on, Spoink, we'll save you!"

They pulled Spoink onto the ferry.
It had lost its pearl underwater
and it was very upset.
"We should try to find that pearl
together," said Brock.
"You're right," said Ash.
"Corphish, let's go!"
He threw a Poké Ball and
released Corphish.
"Mudkip, come on out!" said
Brock, throwing his Poké Ball.

Mudkip and Corphish leapt into
the water. Ash and his friends
waited anxiously on the boat
while their Pokémon searched
the ocean floor.
At last Mudkip and Corphish
reappeared.
"You guys find anything?"
asked Ash. The Pokémon shook
their heads. Poor Spoink looked
very sad.

When they reached Maisie Island, Spoink started hunting for its pearl all over the island. As soon as it saw anything round, it thought that was it! Ash and his friends had a busy time stopping it taking everything it saw. "We've really gotta do something!" Ash groaned. "What's wrong?" asked a voice.

They turned and saw a young man dressed like a scientist walking towards them. "Spoink's pearl fell in the ocean, and now it's lost," Max explained. "I think a Clamperl could help," said the man. "My research shows that Clamperl and Spoink share an interesting relationship. My name's Isaiah. I'm here doing research on Clamperl."

Isaiah took them to his research centre and showed them his Clamperl.

"So what about this relationship between Spoink and Clamperl?" asked Brock.

"The pearl on top of Spoink's heads are created in Clamperl," said Isaiah.

"That's amazing!" cried Ash.

"I wonder if Spoink was coming here to track down a Clamperl," said May.

"Right now none of our Clamperl here are holding pearls," said Isaiah. Spoink started to bounce up and down in front of a glass cabinet. Inside was a beautiful blue pearl. "They're very rare and valuable," Isaiah explained.

The friends left the research centre and walked along the beach. "Don't worry, Spoink," said Ash. "There's gotta be one Clamperl that's holding a pearl."

Back at the research centre, a window opened quietly and three faces peered in at the rare blue pearl.
"Wow, it's gorgeous!" said Jessie.
"That thing must be worth a fortune!" grinned James.
"Let's steal it!" cried Jessie.
They lifted the glass case off the pearl, but before they could grab it, it rose into the air and landed on Spoink's head! Spoink leapt out of the window and escaped – with the pearl!

Ash and his friends heard an alarm go off. They raced back to the research centre. When they arrived at the lab, they found Isaiah talking to some strange-looking cleaners. "These two told me that Spoink made off with the blue pearl!" Isaiah told them.

Jessie and James scurried away.

"Talk about rotten luck!" said Isaiah. "I hadn't even started any of my research!"

"We'd better find that Spoink right away!" cried Ash.

May and Ash sent Beautifly and Swellow to search for Spoink from the air.

"We should split up and look around too!" said Isaiah.

"That was an unwelcome interruption!" said Jessie.
"That bouncing Spoink made total fools outta us!" Meowth agreed.
"Since the pearl is now sitting on Spoink's head, we'll just have to give them both to the boss!"

Meanwhile, Spoink was bouncing down by the seashore, where it met two little children. Spoink was so excited to see them that it tripped and dropped its pearl!
The blue pearl bounced into a nearby Clamperl. It knocked the Clamperl's pink pearl out of the way and took its place. The pink pearl bounced onto Spoink's head!

Soon Beautifly spotted Spoink and led Ash and his friends to it. They got a shock when they saw the pink pearl! "How could Spoink have ended up with a pink one?" asked Isaiah.
The two children walked up to them. "We can tell you," said the boy. "We were over there playing when Spoink tripped and dropped its pearl!"
"It bounced away and then we saw it get switched with the pearl from the Clamperl," said the girl.

Up in a nearby tree, Team Rocket was listening.
"Interesting," smirked Jessie. "So now the blue pearl is inside a Clamperl!"

Spoink led Ash and his friends to the Clamperl that had taken the blue pearl.

"Is that the same one, Spoink?" asked May.

Spoink bounced up to the Clamperl and the shell opened. The friends gasped.

"There it is!" said Isaiah. "My beautiful blue pearl!"

"Excuse me, Clamperl," said May. "It seems you've got that blue pearl by mistake, and we need it back."

The Clamperl didn't like the sound of that.

"Pretty please?" begged Isaiah. Spoink offered its pink pearl back to Clamperl, who agreed. But before they could exchange pearls, a smoke bomb landed next to them!

When the smoke cleared, Team Rocket was standing in front of them!
"Prepare for trouble, we won't be long," said Jessie.
"We'll grab the goodies and soon we'll be gone!" James cheered.
"We want the blue pearl, the Spoink and the Clamperl!" cried Jessie. "Seviper, help me out!"
"I choose you, Torkoal!" cried Ash, releasing Torkoal from the Poké Ball.
"Seviper, use Bite!" Jessie ordered.
"Torkoal, use Iron Defense!" yelled Ash.
Torkoal defended itself well and Seviper fell back.
"Quick, Torkoal, use Flame Thrower now!" Ash cried.
"Seviper, dodge that!" Jessie yelled. "Hit it with a Super Strong Haze and do it now!"
Clouds of black smoke filled the air!

"Protect Clamperl!" yelled Isaiah.
No one could see anything. Brock grabbed Max, thinking he was a Clamperl. Black smoke billowed around them. James appeared next to Jessie with a sack over his shoulder.
"They're all in the bag!" he said smugly.
"Then let's blow this joint!" yelled Meowth.
They leapt aboard their hot-air balloon and rose into the air.

When the smoke cleared, Ash looked around in dismay.
"Where's Spoink?" he asked.
"Standing right here," said May.
"Wait!" cried Isaiah. "Clamperl seems to be missing!"
"We've gotta find 'em!" cried May.

Not far away, the Team Rocket hot-air balloon had landed.
"OK, so I didn't get Spoink," said James. "But two outta three ain't bad!"
"That's assuming there's a blue pearl inside," said Jessie,
knocking on the shell. "Anyone home? Come out and play!"
Clamperl opened and revealed the beautiful blue pearl.
But, before Jessie could grab it, Clamperl shut tight again.
James puffed and panted, but it was no use. He couldn't
prise it open.
"Clamperl love to be sweet talked," said Meowth.
Jessie and James tried to flatter the Clamperl, but it stayed shut.

They tried tickling Clamperl and the shell half opened. But then it clamped down on Meowth's tail!
"YOWEEE!" cried Meowth.
"I believe we're witnessing Clamperl's Clamp Attack!" said James.
Just then, the Clamperl let go and Meowth was catapulted into a tree trunk.
Clamperl hit Jessie with its Water Gun attack and clamped shut again. Jessie flew into a rage and tried to prise Clamperl open.

Not far away, Ash and his friends were searching for Clamperl.
"Man, when we find Team Rocket are they ever gonna regret it!" fumed Ash. Suddenly Swellow flew towards them.
"Did you find 'em?" cried Ash. "Let's go!"

Jessie, James and Meowth were still trying to open Clamperl when Ash and his friends found them. "Stop it!" Ash yelled. "Don't you dare hurt that Clamperl!" added May.

Spoink used its Psybeam to lift Team Rocket away from Clamperl. "Clamperl, are you OK?" asked Ash. Clamperl opened up cautiously. "How dare you?" Jessie shrieked. "Dustox, let's go!" "Cacnea, you too!" added James. "Grovyle, I choose you!" Ash yelled. "Dustox, use Tackle Attack!" cried Jessie. "Grovyle, use Quick Attack!" Ash shouted. Dustox was knocked back.

"OK Cacnea, Pin Missile!" James ordered.
Cacnea hurled an attack at Clamperl,
but Spoink bounced in front of Clamperl
and protected it by using Psychic!
"Grovyle, Bullet Seed, let's go!" cried Ash.
Dustox was thrown back again by Grovyle's
attack. Spoink hit Cacnea with Psybeam.
"Dustox, use your Poison Sting!" Jessie
shouted. Grovyle avoided the attack and
hit Dustox with Leaf Blade.

"Cacnea, Needle Arm – now!" James yelled. But
Spoink sent Cacnea flying with Psybeam. Then
Clamperl used its Water Gun attack to blast Team
Rocket off!

"We did it!" cheered Ash and his friends. "Now
you're safe, Clamperl!"

Clamperl was very grateful to have been rescued!
It exchanged the blue peal with the pink pearl. Isaiah took the blue pearl gladly.
Spoink made a sad noise. It still didn't have a pearl.
"We'll get your pearl back," Ash said. "It's in the ocean somewhere. We'll just keep looking until we find it, OK?"

Clamperl realised that Spoink felt sad.
It offered its beautiful pink pearl to Spoink.
Spoink was delighted!
"That was really nice!" said Ash.

The blue pearl was back at the research centre and Spoink had a brand new pearl!
Ash and his friends were ready to continue their island-hopping adventures!

97 HYPNO
TYPE: Psychic
ABILITY: Insomnia

98 KRABBY
TYPE: Water
ABILITY: Hyper Cutter/Shell Armour

99 KINGLER
TYPE: Water
ABILITY: Hyper Cutter/Shell Armour

100 VOLTORB
TYPE: Electric
ABILITY: Soundproof/Static

101 ELECTRODE
TYPE: Electric
ABILITY: Soundproof/Static

102 EXEGGCUTE
TYPE: Grass/Psychic
ABILITY: Chlorophyll

103 EXEGGUTOR
TYPE: Grass/Psychic
ABILITY: Chlorophyll

104 CUBONE
TYPE: Ground
ABILITY: Rock Head/Lightningrod

105 MAROWAK
TYPE: Ground
ABILITY: Rock Head/Lightningrod

106 HITMONLEE
TYPE: Fighting
ABILITY: Limber

107 HITMONCHAN
TYPE: Fighting
ABILITY: Keen Eye

108 LICKITUNG
TYPE: Normal
ABILITY: Own Tempo/Oblivious

109 KOFFING
TYPE: Poison
ABILITY: Levitate

110 WEEZING
TYPE: Poison
ABILITY: Levitate

111 RHYHORN
TYPE: Ground/Rock
ABILITY: Lightningrod/Rock Head

112 RHYDON
TYPE: Ground/Rock
ABILITY: Lightningrod/Rock Head

113 CHANSEY
TYPE: Normal
ABILITY: Natural Cure/Serene Grace

114 TANGELA
TYPE: Grass
ABILITY: Chlorophyll

115 KANGASKHAN
TYPE: Normal
ABILITY: Early Bird

116 HORSEA
TYPE: Water
ABILITY: Swift Swim

117 SEADRA
TYPE: Water
ABILITY: Poison Point

118 GOLDEEN
TYPE: Water
ABILITY: Swift Swim/Water Veil

119 SEAKING
TYPE: Water
ABILITY: Swift Swim/Water Veil

120 STARYU
TYPE: Water
ABILITY: Illuminate/Natural Cure

121 STARMIE
TYPE: Water/Psychic
ABILITY: Illuminate/Natural Cure

122 MR. MIME
TYPE: Psychic
ABILITY: Soundproof

123 SCYTHER
TYPE: Bug/Flying
ABILITY: Swarm

124 JYNX
TYPE: Ice/Psychic
ABILITY: Oblivious

125 ELECTABUZZ
TYPE: Electric
ABILITY: Static

126 MAGMAR
TYPE: Fire
ABILITY: Flame Body

127 PINSIR
TYPE: Bug
ABILITY: Hyper Cutter

128 TAUROS
TYPE: Normal
ABILITY: Intimidate

129 MAGIKARP
TYPE: Water
ABILITY: Swift Swim

130 GYARADOS
TYPE: Water/Flying
ABILITY: Intimidate

131 LAPRAS
TYPE: Water/Ice
ABILITY: Water Absorb/Shell Armour

132 DITTO
TYPE: Normal
ABILITY: Limber

133 EEVEE
TYPE: Normal
ABILITY: Run Away

134 VAPOREON
TYPE: Water
ABILITY: Water Absorb

135 JOLTEON
TYPE: Electric
ABILITY: Volt Absorb

136 FLAREON
TYPE: Fire
ABILITY: Flash Fire

137 PORYGON
TYPE: Normal
ABILITY: Trace

138 OMANYTE
TYPE: Rock/Water
ABILITY: Swift Swim/Shell Armour

139 OMASTAR
TYPE: Rock/Water
ABILITY: Swift Swim/Shell Armour

140 KABUTO
TYPE: Rock/Water
ABILITY: Swift Swim/Battle Armour

141 KABUTOPS
TYPE: Rock/Water
ABILITY: Swift Swim/Battle Armour

142 AERODACTYL
TYPE: Rock/Flying
ABILITY: Rock Head/Pressure

143 SNORLAX
TYPE: Normal
ABILITY: Immunity/Thick Fat

144 ARTICUNO
TYPE: Ice/Flying
ABILITY: Pressure

145 ZAPDOS
TYPE: Electric/Flying
ABILITY: Pressure

146 MOLTRES
TYPE: Fire/Flying
ABILITY: Pressure

147 DRATINI
TYPE: Dragon
ABILITY: Shed Skin

148 DRAGONAIR
TYPE: Dragon
ABILITY: Shed Skin

149 DRAGONITE
TYPE: Dragon/Flying
ABILITY: Inner Focus

150 MEWTWO
TYPE: Psychic
ABILITY: Pressure

151 MEW
TYPE: Psychic
ABILITY: Synchronize

152 CHIKORITA
TYPE: Grass
ABILITY: Overgrow

153 BAYLEEF
TYPE: Grass
ABILITY: Overgrow

154 MEGANIUM
TYPE: Grass
ABILITY: Overgrow

155 CYNDAQUIL
TYPE: Fire
ABILITY: Blaze

156 QUILAVA
TYPE: Fire
ABILITY: Blaze

157 TYPHLOSION
TYPE: Fire
ABILITY: Blaze

158 TOTODILE
TYPE: Water
ABILITY: Torrent

159 CROCONAW
TYPE: Water
ABILITY: Torrent

160 FERALIGATR
TYPE: Water
ABILITY: Torrent

161 SENTRET
TYPE: Normal
ABILITY: Run Away/Keen Eye

162 FURRET
TYPE: Normal
ABILITY: Run Away/Keen Eye

163 HOOTHOOT
TYPE: Normal/Flying
ABILITY: Insomnia/Keen Eye

164 NOCTOWL
TYPE: Normal/Flying
ABILITY: Insomnia/Keen Eye

165 LEDYBA
TYPE: Bug/Flying
ABILITY: Swarm/Early Bird

166 LEDIAN
TYPE: Bug/Flying
ABILITY: Swarm/Early Bird

167 SPINARAK
TYPE: Bug/Poison
ABILITY: Swarm/Insomnia

168 ARIADOS
TYPE: Bug/Poison
ABILITY: Swarm/Insomnia

169 CROBAT
TYPE: Poison/Flying
ABILITY: Inner Focus

170 CHINCHOU
TYPE: Water/Electric
ABILITY: Volt Absorb/Illuminate

171 LANTURN
TYPE: Water/Electric
ABILITY: Volt Absorb/Illuminate

172 PICHU
TYPE: Electric
ABILITY: Static

173 CLEFFA
TYPE: Normal
ABILITY: Cute Charm

174 IGGLYBUFF
TYPE: Normal
ABILITY: Cute Charm

175 TOGEPI
TYPE: Normal
ABILITY: Hustle/Serene Grace

176 TOGETIC
TYPE: Normal/Flying
ABILITY: Hustle/Serene Grace

177 NATU
TYPE: Psychic/Flying
ABILITY: Synchronize/Early Bird

178 XATU
TYPE: Psychic/Flying
ABILITY: Synchronize/Early Bird

179 MAREEP
TYPE: Electric
ABILITY: Static

180 FLAAFFY
TYPE: Electric
ABILITY: Static

181 AMPHAROS
TYPE: Electric
ABILITY: Static

182 BELLOSSOM
TYPE: Grass
ABILITY: Chlorophyll

183 MARILL
TYPE: Water
ABILITY: Thick Fat/Huge Power

184 AZUMARILL
TYPE: Water
ABILITY: Thick Fat/Huge Power

185 SUDOWOODO
TYPE: Rock
ABILITY: Sturdy/Rock Head

186 POLITOED
TYPE: Water
ABILITY: Water Absorb/Damp

187 HOPPIP
TYPE: Grass/Flying
ABILITY: Chlorophyll

188 SKIPLOOM
TYPE: Grass/Flying
ABILITY: Chlorophyll

189 JUMPLUFF
TYPE: Grass/Flying
ABILITY: Chlorophyll

190 AIPOM
TYPE: Normal
ABILITY: Run Away/Pickup

191 SUNKERN
TYPE: Grass
ABILITY: Chlorophyll

192 SUNFLORA
TYPE: Grass
ABILITY: Chlorophyll

The Amazing World of Pokémon!

Great explorers draw maps to guide others through the dangers they have faced. Ash's adventures have taken him through many regions and he has seen some awesome places!
Use these maps to trace his journeys.

Hoenn

Johto

Kanto

#325 SPOINK

Type: Psychic
Height: 0.7km

Spoink bounces around on its tail and the shock of this bouncing makes its heart pump. It cannot afford to stop bouncing because if it stops, its heart will stop

Ability: Thick Fat/Own Tempo
Weight: 30.6kg

#366 CLAMPERL

Type: Water
Height: 0.4km

Clamperl grows inside the protection of its shell and is ready to evolve when it becomes too large for it. It also uses its shell for clamping and catching prey.

Ability: Shell Amour
Weight: 52.5kg

#388 GOREBYSS

Type: Water
Height: 1.8km

Gorebyss is beautiful and elegant but it is also very cruel. It puts its thin mouth into its prey's body and drains away its body fluids.

Ability: Swift Swim
Weight: 22.6kg

#387 HUNTAIL

Type: Water
Height: 1.7km

Huntail lives in the murky depths of the ocean. It uses its tail to attract prey and swims by wiggling its slender body like a snake.

Ability: Swift Swim
Weight: 27.kg

THE RELICANTH REALLY CAN

While exploring islands on their way to Mossdeep City, Ash and his friends found themselves on Wazoo Island. Suddenly they saw a figure rising out of the sea, draped in seaweed!

"What is that?" cried Ash.

"A – a sea monster?" whimpered May.

"Adam, man of the sea, has found his buried treasure!" cried the figure, pulling off the seaweed. It was a man! He threw a sack down beside him, reached into it and pulled out a string of glittering green jewels!

"They're beautiful!" said May.
"They look like they're old, too – they could be valuable!" said Brock.
"I'm sure about that!" said Adam. "These will be the prize items in my shop!"

Adam took the friends to see his shop. He introduced them to his wife, Evelyn, and showed her his treasure. Evelyn told him that they were just green shards and not very valuable.
"Long ago, green shards were used in making jewellery," she explained.
Adam looked sad.
"How do you suppose they ended up at the bottom of the ocean?" asked Brock.
"I'm hoping they're from the wreck of the King Neptune," said Adam. "It's a famous sunken ship."

"The King Neptune was caught in a typhoon, right off the coast of this island," Adam explained. "The ship sank to the bottom of the sea. For one hundred years now, no one has been able to find it. According to the legend, the King Neptune carried the greatest treasure ever to set sail."

"Do you think that you can remember where you found this?" asked Ash.
"It was my last dive of the day," said Adam. "I happened to catch sight of a Relicanth. Something was caught on its fin and, as it swam off, it fell off right into my hands."

"That Relicanth might just lead us to the Neptune if you can find it again," said Evelyn.
"I can find it again!" Adam exclaimed. "I won't quit until that lost treasure's mine at last!"
"Would you mind if we all came along and helped you?" asked Ash.
"That sounds good!" said Adam. "Evelyn, is the ship ready?"
"Aye aye, sir!" smiled Evelyn. "I'll just refuel the submarine and then we can set off!"

Outside the window, Team Rocket had been eavesdropping.
"Sunken treasure, eh?" mused Jessie.
"And the best kind, too," said James. "The kind they go and find for us!"

Ash and his friends were soon out at sea with Adam and Evelyn. Evelyn stayed in the main boat while the others dived down in the submarine. The submarine dived slowly into the depths of the ocean. "Now you're gonna see some things you've never seen before!" Adam told them.

They saw lots of rare and unusual Pokémon swimming past the submarine.
"I didn't know there were Pokémon this deep in the ocean!" Ash gasped.
"Look, there's a school of Chinchou over there!" said Max.
Just then, the sonar detector screen began to flash. It had picked up the Relicanth ahead of them. But then the submarine was rammed from behind!

"I'll check the rear view!" cried Adam. He flicked on the screen and they saw what looked like an enormous Magikarp ramming the back of the submarine!
"That's Team Rocket's submarine!" Ash yelled.
"Team Rocket?" asked Adam.
"They're troublemakers who use Pokémon for evil purposes!" Brock explained.
"They must have heard about the treasure," groaned Ash.

Team Rocket fired two rockets at them! Adam's submarine was blown sideways by the blast and Team Rocket raced past.
"Those guys really make me mad!" said Max.
"No way are they getting that treasure!" May added.

Team Rocket was still chasing the Relicanth. Their submarine plunged deeper and deeper into the ocean. But it was starting to leak! Suddenly the submarine began to flood with water. It was dragged even deeper into the ocean. Team Rocket was swept away!

Adam's submarine caught up with the Relicanth and saw it swim into an underwater tunnel. There was a powerful current and the Relicanth dived into it. Adam followed it in!
"This is the strongest current I've ever felt!" yelled Adam, struggling to steady the submarine. They were whirled along the rocky tunnel – but where were they going?

The submarine finally stopped. Pikachu leapt into Ash's arms. "Looks like the submarine is still intact," said Brock. "Yeah, but where exactly did we end up?" asked Ash. Then he glanced out of the window and gave a yell of excitement. They were next to a huge wreck of an old-fashioned ship! "Adam, could this be the wreck you told us about?" asked Ash.

They stepped out of the submarine. They were on a small beach in the underwater cave, at the edge of a lake.
"That's it!" cried Adam. "I'm sure that's the King Neptune from the legend! I'm going in and getting that treasure!"

Adam raced over to the ship and jumped on board. Ash and his friends looked around.

"I wonder how there can be so much light in here if we're in an underwater cavern," said Max.

"And somehow there's fresh air coming in here too," May added.

"Hey look," said Ash, pointing. "Maybe the air comes in through that big opening over there!"

"Hmm," said Brock. "That's the only one I see, so I guess that's how we came in."

"Which means that in order for us to leave, we'll have to go back through there again," groaned May.

Suddenly the friends noticed several Relicanth swimming around the wrecked ship.

"I dunno about treasure, but that ship sure has a lot of Relicanth," said Max.

Just then there was a yell from the ship and Adam appeared with a treasure chest.

"Looks like you were right, Adam!" called Ash.

"Come on, let's take a look at it!" said Max eagerly.

"All right," said Adam. "I'm opening it up!"

"No you're not!" yelled a familiar voice. It was Jessie and the rest of Team Rocket!

"We do appreciate your going to the trouble of finding the treasure for us!" Jessie smirked. Meowth pressed a button and a wire shot out of the Team Rocket submarine and took the treasure chest!

Adam raced towards them, but they fired two missiles at him and he had to duck to avoid them. The missiles blasted into the King Neptune instead!
"They blew up the ship!" cried Adam.
"And they destroyed where all of the Relicanth were living!" Ash yelled.

The Relicanth were very angry but Team Rocket fired two more missiles – straight at them! "Corphish, GO!" Ash yelled. Corphish hit the missiles with its Bubble Beam and destroyed them.

Team Rocket jumped back into their submarine and escaped up the tunnel. Meowth fired two missiles into the roof of the tunnel and blocked the exit with rubble. Ash and his friends were trapped!

"How are we supposed to get outta this place now?" Max cried.
Just then the Relicanth started to move.
"Where are they heading off to?" wondered May.
"They know another opening and they wanna show us the way!" guessed Brock.
"Back into the sub, everybody!" Adam ordered. "We're following the Relicanth!"

They joined the Relicanth and dived down into the water. At last they saw another exit up ahead!
"We're gonna have to go through a pretty strong current!" Brock gasped.
"Don't worry!" said Adam. "I'll get all of you home safe. Hold on!"
The submarine shook and rattled as it entered the powerful current.

Up on the boat, Evelyn was worried. It had been over an hour with no communication from the submarine. Then, suddenly, the radio crackled. "Submarine to Evelyn!" said a familiar voice. "We've had a close call, but we're returning to surface. Thanks to our Relicanth escort, we're on our way back home!"

Soon, Ash and his friends were back on board the boat. The Relicanth gathered around them in the water. "Thank you!" Ash called to them. "You were awesome!"
Adam told Evelyn about how Team Rocket had stolen the treasure. "Then it's lucky for you that I've been tracking them the whole time!" Evelyn grinned.

Not far away, Team Rocket had just landed their submarine on a secluded beach.
"I can't believe one of our plans actually worked for a change!" said Jessie.
"All we have to do now is get this treasure chest off to the boss – and then let the
good times roll!" James grinned.

"Not so fast!" yelled a voice. It was Ash and his friends on Adam's boat, surrounded by the Relicanth!
"Give the treasure back to Adam or you're gonna be sorry!" Ash shouted.
"But we sealed them in the cave!" said James. "How'd they get out?"

"Bulbasaur, let's go!" cried May. Bulbasaur threw its vines around the chest, but Team Rocket clung on to it. "Get your vines off my treasure!" shouted Jessie. "Go, Seviper! Lay out that Bulbasaur with your Poison Tail!" "Cover Bulbasaur with your Water Gun, Mudkip!" yelled Brock.

As Mudkip blasted Seviper with its Water gun, the Relicanth hit Team Rocket with their Hydro Pump! Bulbasaur took the chance to grab the treasure chest and passed it to Adam. "Pikachu, finish it up with Thunder!" cried Ash. Team Rocket blasted off again!

"Well, shall we have a look at this treasure?" said Adam. Everyone gathered around in excitement. Adam lifted the lid and gasped.

"It's all green shards!" he exclaimed. "Just lots and lots of green shards!"

"Why was the ship carrying so may of 'em?" asked Ash.

"Well," said Brock. "Probably because they were used for making jewellery back then, they were worth a lot more than they are now!"

"I was so certain I'd found treasure!" sighed Adam.

"Don't be sad!" Evelyn smiled. "All those green shards will make a lot of beautiful jewellery that we can sell!"

"I guess you're right," said Adam, cheering up.

"I think shards are beautiful!" squealed May.

"I'll make sure we give you the very first necklace we finish," Evelyn promised.

Adam looked out at the ocean. "The sea is still full of mysteries," he said. "There's still treasure out there for those who seek it!"

Make your own Pokémon card holder

All good Pokémon trainers have to have their cards close by – you never know when you might be challenged to do battle!

Follow the instructions and make this holder for your Pokémon cards – you'll always be ready for battle!

What you will need:

Tracing paper
Cardboard
Scissors
Velcro
Strong glue
An adult to help you

What to do:

Trace the shape onto a piece of strong cardboard. You can use coloured cardboard if you would like a bright card holder!

Ask an adult to help you cut out the shape. Cut along the small dotted lines and fold along the large dotted lines.

Glue the areas as shown and stick them together.

Cut out a circle from the Velcro. This will be the fastener for your card case. Stick it on the case where the pink circles are shown.

Now you can decorate your case! Draw a picture of your favourite Pokémon (see page 14 for how to draw Pikachu) or cut out some pictures and glue them on. You could write your name on the case – or make one for each of your Pokémon trainer friends!

Fold these lines – – – – – –

Cut these lines ·········

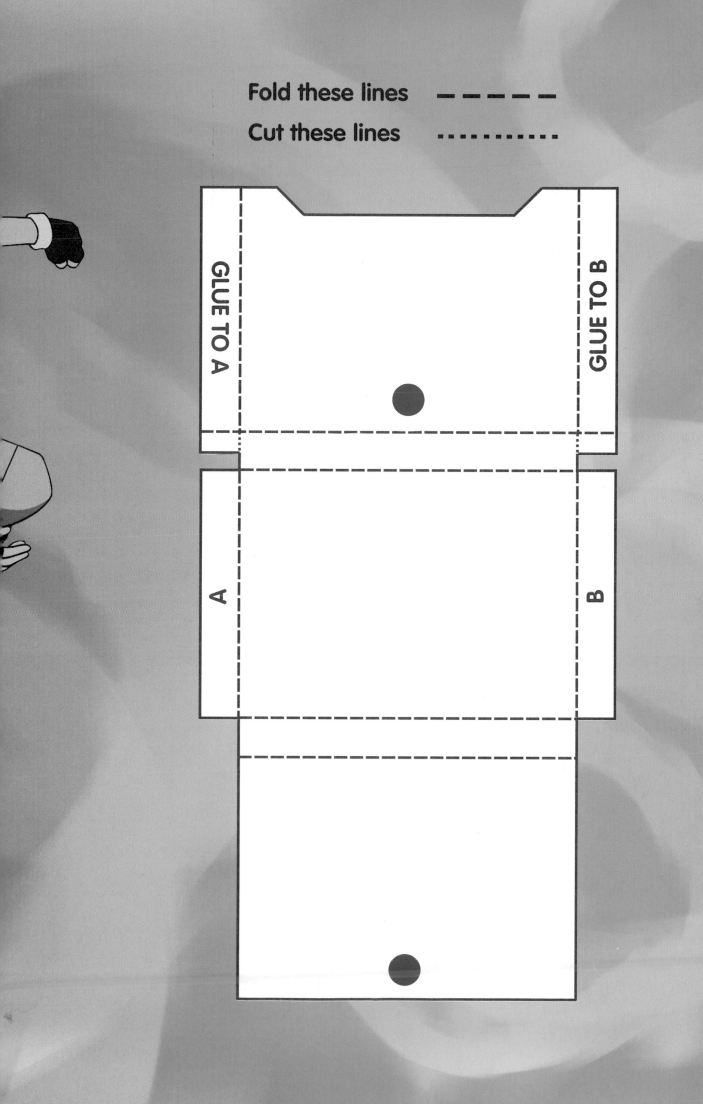

GLUE TO A

GLUE TO B

A

B

57

Part 2 ARE YOU A POKÉMON MASTER?

Training to become a Pokémon Master is not an easy task. There are many challenges to face and battles to engage. But with a true heart and a brave spirit, you will always have a chance! Stay calm and answer these questions to discover your destiny!

1. What does a Squirtle squirt?

A. Water ☐
B. Fire ☐
C. Air ☐

2. What colour is Luvdisk?

A. Red ☐
B. Pink ☐
C. Blue ☐

3. Which two Pokémon are covered in prickles?

A. Bulbasaur and Ivysaur ☐
B. Charmeleon and Charizard ☐
C. Cacnea and Cacturne ☐

4. What type of Pokémon is Golduck?

A. Water ☐
B. Grass ☐
C. Poison ☐

5. Name this Pokémon?

A. Dugtrio ☐
B. Zigzagoon ☐
C. Cubone ☐

6. How many badges do you need to win to enter the Hoenn Pokémon League?

A. 7 ☐
B. 6 ☐
C. 8 ☐

Now check your answers. Each correct answer earns one point. Keep a note of your score – your test will continue later!

ANSWERS: 1.Water 2.Pink 3.Cacnea and Cacturne 4.Water 5.Zigzagoon 6.8

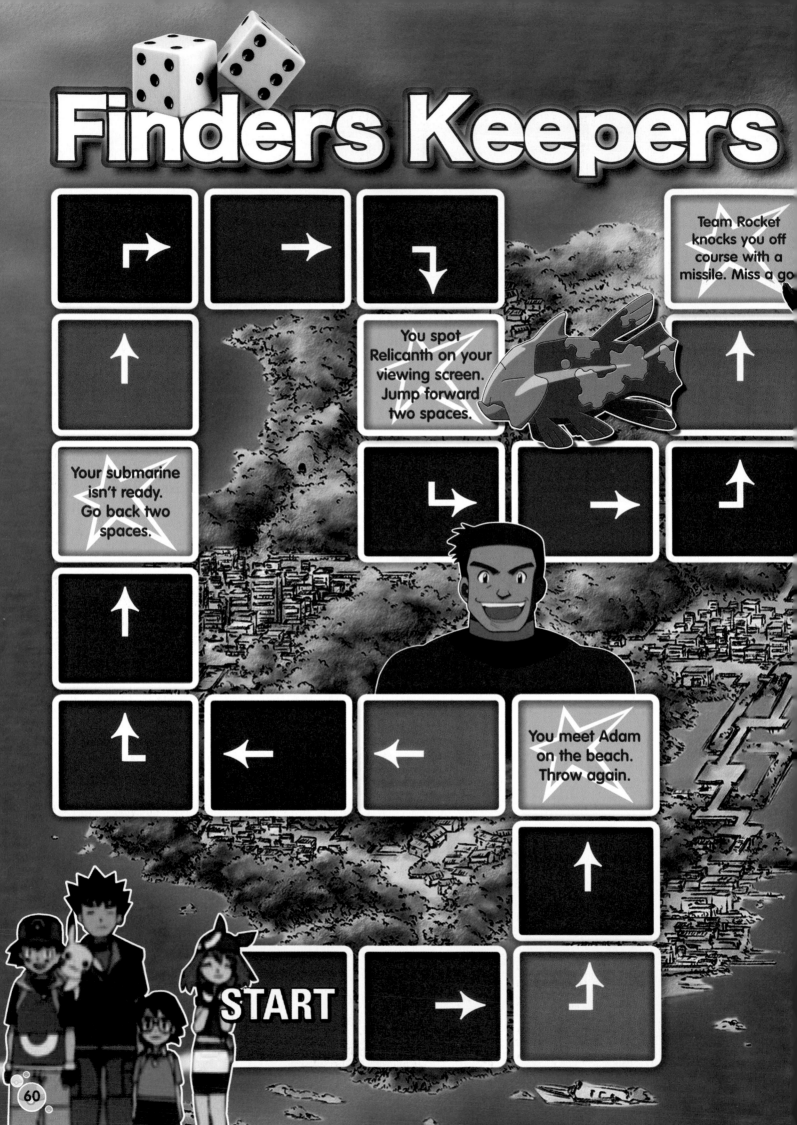

Join Ash and his friends as they try to reach the King Neptune before bumbling Team Rocket. Journey to Wazoo Island on the ferry and work your way towards the treasure chest on board the shipwreck!

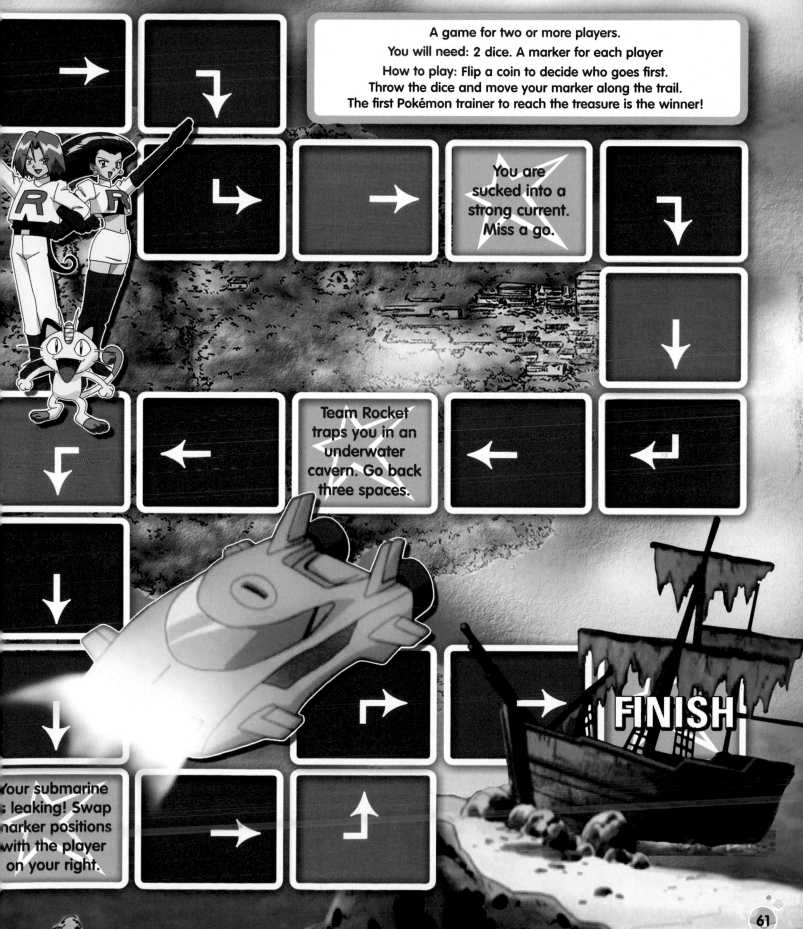

A game for two or more players.
You will need: 2 dice. A marker for each player
How to play: Flip a coin to decide who goes first.
Throw the dice and move your marker along the trail.
The first Pokémon trainer to reach the treasure is the winner!

You are sucked into a strong current. Miss a go.

Team Rocket traps you in an underwater cavern. Go back three spaces.

FINISH

Your submarine is leaking! Swap marker positions with the player on your right.

THE EVOLUTIONARY WAR

Ash and his friends were on the ferry, enjoying being at sea. "Hey Brock, which island is coming up next?" asked Ash. "The ABCs," said Brock. "It's three islands that are grouped together called the A, B and C," explained Max. "Which one are we heading for?" asked May. "We should probably stop at Island A first," said Brock. "That's the only one that has a Pokémon Centre."

As the ferry got closer to Island A, a group of children overtook it. Some of them were riding speeders. Some were riding Gorebyss Pokémon and some were riding Huntail Pokémon. They were all shouting and arguing.

As Ash and his friends watched, a boy on Gorebyss knocked into a girl on Huntail. She fell into the water.
"Are you all right?" gasped Ash as the ferry stopped beside her.
"I'm fine!" she snapped.
"Huntail, let's go!"

Nearby, a periscope stuck out of the water. Below, Jessie, James and Meowth were in the Team Rocket submarine.
"Seems like the twerps are headed off to another little island," said Jessie thoughtfully.

On Island A, Ash and his friends walked into the Pokémon Centre and saw Nurse Joy.

Just then, the videophone began to ring. It was a lady with an ill Corsola. "I'm afraid it may have caught a bad cold," said the lady. "Could I send it over and have you take a look?"

"Of course," smiled Nurse Joy. The machine next to the videophone crackled and a Poké Ball appeared on it. "So they've got a teleporter on Island B?" Max gasped.

"That's right," said Nurse Joy. "Island A is the only island with a Pokémon Centre, so we've set up teleporters on islands B and C."

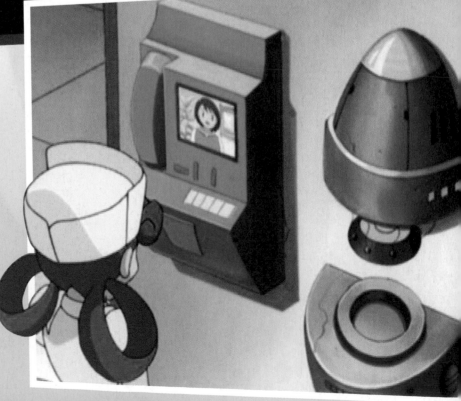

Just then they heard shouting and angry voices.

"Oh no, here we go again," sighed Nurse Joy. It was the same group of children they had seen fighting earlier. They were in a classroom in the middle of the Pokémon Centre.

"Gorebyss are much stronger and you know it!" hollered a boy.

"You're crazy, Huntail are!" screamed a girl.

"Everyone, quiet down this minute!" said Nurse Joy crossly.

"Is this some kinda school?" asked Ash.

"It's a school as well as a Pokémon Centre," Nurse Joy explained.

"Students, our next class will be held at the outdoor pool."

Nurse Joy led Ash and his friends to the pool. "The kids from islands B and C have developed a real rivalry," said Nurse Joy. "For some reason Clamperl evolve into Gorebyss on Island B and into Huntail on Island C. Adults and kids are always arguing about which are better – Gorebyss or Huntail."

At the pool, a man was floating in the water, surrounded by Huntail and Gorebyss. "Hey mister, aren't Huntail better than Gorebyss?" called a girl. "Gorebyss are way better, right?" asked a boy. "I think both Pokémon are great!" smiled the man. Ash gasped. It was Professor Birch!

Professor Birch climbed out of the pool.

"I'm here doing research on the way Clamperl evolve," he said.

"People around here say that Clamperl evolve into Gorebyss on Island B and into Huntail on Island C," May told him.

"Is that so?" asked Professor Birch. "In order for a Clamperl to evolve into a Huntail, a deepseatooth is needed, while a deepseascale is necessary for a Clamperl to evolve into a Gorebyss."

"What do they have to do with evolving?" asked Max.

"That's what I want to know," said Professor Birch. "First I'm going to Island C."

"Professor, could we go along with you?" asked Ash.

"Sure!" grinned Professor Birch.

Soon they were all together in a speedboat.
"Wait!" called a little girl, jumping into the
boat with them. "Let me show you around
Island C!"
Professor Birch agreed and they set off.

On Island C the girl, whose name was Nancy,
led them to a rocky cavern.
There was a small waterfall inside.
"My grandma used to tell me that if you
brought a Clamperl into this cavern, it'd turn
into a Huntail in no time at all!" she said.
"Fascinating," murmured Professor Birch,
tasting the water. "It's delicious and very rich
in minerals."
"There must be some secret to the water,"
said May.
"I'll take a little sample," said Professor Birch.

He filled a sample jar with the water. Suddenly they heard a footstep behind them. It was Keith, from Island B!

"What are you doing here?" snapped Nancy. "Kids from Island B aren't allowed on Island C!"

"I just came here to do a little research on my enemies," said Keith.

"Then you must be interested in Huntail?" said Professor Birch.

"I don't care about Huntail!" said the boy, turning red. "I only like Gorebyss!"

"I'm doing my next research on Gorebyss," said Professor Birch. "How about being my Island B guide?"

"Yeah!" cried the boy. "Sure!"

On Island B, Keith showed them a cavern.
"My grandpa used to tell me that if you brought Clamperl into this cave, they'd turn into Gorebyss," he said.
There was a waterfall here too. Professor Birch tasted the water.
"It's a bit different, but still rich in minerals and quite delicious," he said.
He took a sample. Then they heard a footstep behind them. It was Nancy!

"Hey!" snapped Keith. "We're researching Gorebyss, so it's none of your business!"
"I'm just checking out the competition!" Nancy retorted.
"I guess that means you're interested in Gorebyss?" asked Professor Birch.
"No!" she shrieked, turning red. She turned and ran out of the cave.

Back on Island A, Professor Birch studied the samples he had taken.

"I've learnt one interesting thing," he said. But before he could say any more, Nancy and Keith ran up to him.

"Professor! Please tell me what you learnt about Gorebyss!" cried Nancy.

"No, talk about Huntail!" Keith begged.

"Seems to me that Nancy likes Gorebyss and Keith likes Huntail!" smiled May. "Am I right?"

The children nodded. They both looked embarrassed.

"Is that why you guys are fighting so much?" asked Ash.

"I really want my Clamperl to evolve into a Gorebyss" sighed Nancy.

"And I want a Huntail!" added Keith.

They went out to the pool and showed Professor Birch their Clamperl. A Gorebyss and Huntail were doing laps in the pool.

"It's best for both the trainer and the Pokémon if it evolves into the Pokémon you really want," said Professor Birch.

"Have you figured out how they evolve?" asked Nancy.

"The water in both caves comes from deep under the sea," said Professor Birch. "The water from Island C contains particles of deepseatooth. The water from Island B contains particles of deepseascale."

Team Rocket was watching the Gorebyss and Huntail.
"Those are the perfect gift for the boss!" Meowth chuckled.
"I've got the perfect plan!" smirked Jessie.

Suddenly Team Rocket's submarine rose out of the water.
Meowth hurled a net at the Gorebyss and Huntail!
"Go, Corphish!" Ash yelled. Corphish cut the net and freed
the Pokémon.
"Oh no you don't!" Jessie seethed. "Seviper, Fight Attack!"
But Corphish knocked Seviper back into the water.

"Cacnea, go!" ordered James.
"Pin Missile!"
"Clamperl, Water Gun!" yelled
Nancy and Keith together. Their
Clamperl forced Team Rocket back
with two powerful jets of water.
"Go, Pikachu!" Ash cried.
"Pika!" agreed Pikachu, firing a
Thunderbolt. Team Rocket was
driven away!

Professor Birch decided to
explore the caverns again.
In the cavern on Island B, Keith
found a deepseascale. He gave
it to Nancy.
"Since you want your Clamperl
to become a Gorebyss, it's
yours," he smiled.
But when Nancy gave the scale
to her Clamperl, nothing
happened! So she teleported
her Clamperl across to the
Pokémon Centre.

In the cavern on Island C, Nancy found a deepseatooth. She gave it to Keith.
"Since you want your Clamperl to be a Huntail, here," she said.
He gave the tooth to his Clamperl, but nothing happened!
Keith used the teleporter to send the Clamperl to the Pokémon Centre.

Later, back at the Pokémon Centre, Professor Birch asked Nancy and Keith to fetch their Pokémon. They were still Clamperl!
"Doesn't look like anything happened," said Ash.
But just then the Clamperl started to glow.
"Is this it?" gasped Keith.
Ash and his friends watched in awe as the two Clamperl evolved into Gorebyss and Huntail.

"My Clamperl is a Gorebyss!" Nancy cried in delight.
"And mine evolved into a Huntail!" grinned Keith.
"I wonder what took 'em so long to evolve?" said Max.
"There is always more to learn about Pokémon!" said Professor Birch.
"What about taking them out for a swim?" May suggested.

Nancy's Gorebyss and Keith's Huntail played happily together in the water.
Suddenly there was a huge eruption in the water. Team Rocket was back!
This time they had a bigger and better submarine. It was a huge model of a Kingler!
"Our hyper-alloy Kingler will catch those Pokémon in a flash!" sniggered Meowth.

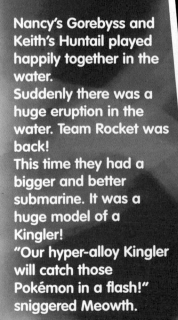

"Gorebyss, Agility!" Nancy cried, as a huge arm came down to grab her Pokémon. "Huntail, Bite, let's go!" yelled Keith. Their Pokémon obeyed, but they were no match for the huge machine! "Grovyle, I choose you!" Ash yelled. "Bullet Seed, go!" But even Grovyle's attack couldn't harm the vessel!

Meowth threw a net around Gorebyss and Huntail. But Grovyle cut the net and freed the Pokémon.
"Gorebyss, use Confusion!" Nancy cried.
Team Rocket was thrown into confusion. Then Pikachu blasted them with Thunder!
"Use Screech Attack, Huntail!" cried Keith.
The terrible sound sent Team Rocket blasting off again!

"Can you believe how super strong Gorebyss are?" said Nancy.
"Don't forget about Huntail too!" said Keith.
"It's obvious you've been taking the time to study up on Gorebyss and Huntail attacks," smiled May.
Ash and his friends said goodbye to all their new friends and set off again on the ferry.
Miracles never cease in the world of Pokémon!

193 YANMA
TYPE: Bug/Flying
ABILITY: Speed Boost/ Compoundeyes

194 WOOPER
TYPE: Water/Ground
ABILITY: Damp/Water Absorb

195 QUAGSIRE
TYPE: Water/Ground
ABILITY: Damp/Water Absorb

196 ESPEON
TYPE: Psychic
ABILITY: Synchronize

197 UMBREON
TYPE: Dark
ABILITY: Synchronize

198 MURKROW
TYPE: Dark/Flying
ABILITY: Insomnia

199 SLOWKING
TYPE: Water/Psychic
ABILITY: Oblivious/Own Tempo

200 MISDREAVUS
TYPE: Ghost
ABILITY: Levitate

201 UNOWN
TYPE: Psychic
ABILITY: Levitate

202 WOBBUFFET
TYPE: Psychic
ABILITY: Shadow Tag

203 GIRAFARIG
TYPE: Normal/Psychic
ABILITY: Inner Focus/Early Bird

204 PINECO
TYPE: Bug
ABILITY: Sturdy

205 FORRETRESS
TYPE: Bug/Steel
ABILITY: Sturdy

206 DUNSPARCE
TYPE: Normal
ABILITY: Serene Grace/Run Away

207 GLIGAR
TYPE: Ground/Flying
ABILITY: Hyper Cutter/Sand Veil

208 STEELIX
TYPE: Steel/Ground
ABILITY: Rock Head/Sturdy

209 SNUBBULL
TYPE: Normal
ABILITY: Intimidate/Run Away

210 GRANBULL
TYPE: Normal
ABILITY: Intimidate/Run Away

211 QWILFISH
TYPE: Water/Poison
ABILITY: Poison Point/Swift Swim

212 SCIZOR
TYPE: Bug/Steel
ABILITY: Swarm

213 SHUCKLE
TYPE: Bug/Rock
ABILITY: Sturdy

214 HERACROSS
TYPE: Bug/Fighting
ABILITY: Swarm/Guts

215 SNEASEL
TYPE: Dark Ice
ABILITY: Inner Focus/Keen Eye

216 TEDDIURSA
TYPE: Normal
ABILITY: Pickup

217 URSARING
TYPE: Normal
ABILITY: Guts

218 SLUGMA
TYPE: Fire
ABILITY: Magma Armour/Flame Body

219 MAGCARGO
TYPE: Fire/Rock
ABILITY: Magma Armour/Flame Body

220 SWINUB
TYPE: Ice/Ground
ABILITY: Oblivious

221 PILOSWINE
TYPE: Ice/Ground
ABILITY: Oblivious

222 CORSOLA
TYPE: Water/Rock
ABILITY: Hustle/Natural Cure

223 REMORAID
TYPE: Water
ABILITY: Hustle

224 OCTILLERY
TYPE: Water
ABILITY: Suction Cups

225 DELIBIRD
TYPE: Ice/Flying
ABILITY: Vital Spirit/Hustle

226 MANTINE
TYPE: Water/Flying
ABILITY: Swift Swim/Water Absorb

227 SKARMORY
TYPE: Steel/Flying
ABILITY: Keen Eye/Sturdy

228 HOUNDOUR
TYPE: Dark/Fire
ABILITY: Early Bird/Flash Fire

229 HOUNDOOM
TYPE: Dark/Fire
ABILITY: Early Bird/Flash Fire

230 KINGDRA
TYPE: Water/Dragon
ABILITY: Swift Swim

231 PHANPY
TYPE: Ground
ABILITY: Pickup

232 DONPHAN
TYPE: Ground
ABILITY: Sturdy

233 PORYGON2
TYPE: Normal
ABILITY: Trace

234 STANTLER
TYPE: Normal
ABILITY: Intimidate

235 SMEARGLE
TYPE: Normal
ABILITY: Own Tempo

236 TYROGUE
TYPE: Fighting
ABILITY: Guts

237 HITMONTOP
TYPE: Fighting
ABILITY: Intimidate

238 SMOOCHUM
TYPE: Ice/Psychic
ABILITY: Oblivious

239 ELEKID
TYPE: Electric
ABILITY: Static

240 MAGBY
TYPE: Fire
ABILITY: Flame Body

241 MILTANK
TYPE: Normal
ABILITY: Thick Fat

242 BLISSEY
TYPE: Normal
ABILITY: Natural Cure/Serene Grace

243 RAIKOU
TYPE: Electric
ABILITY: Pressure

244 ENTEI
TYPE: Fire
ABILITY: Pressure

245 SUICUNE
TYPE: Water
ABILITY: Pressure

246 LARVITAR
TYPE: Rock/Ground
ABILITY: Guts

247 PUPITAR
TYPE: Rock/Ground
ABILITY: Shed Skin

248 TYRANITAR
TYPE: Dark/Rock
ABILITY: Sand Stream

249 LUGIA
TYPE: Psychic/Flying
ABILITY: Pressure

250 HO-OH
TYPE: Fire/Flying
ABILITY: Pressure

251 CELEBI
TYPE: Grass/Psychic
ABILITY: Natural Cure

252 TREECKO
TYPE: Grass
ABILITY: Overgrow

253 GROVYLE
TYPE: Grass
ABILITY: Overgrow

254 SCEPTILE
TYPE: Grass
ABILITY: Overgrow

255 TORCHIC
TYPE: Fire
ABILITY: Blaze

256 COMBUSKEN
TYPE: Fire/Fighting
ABILITY: Blaze

257 BLAZIKEN
TYPE: Fire/Fighting
ABILITY: Blaze

258 MUDKIP
TYPE: Water
ABILITY: Torrent

259 MARSHTOMP
TYPE: Water/Ground
ABILITY: Torrent

260 SWAMPERT
TYPE: Water/Ground
ABILITY: Torrent

261 POOCHYENA
TYPE: Dark
ABILITY: Run Away

262 MIGHTYENA
TYPE: Dark
ABILITY: Intimidate

263 ZIGZAGOON
TYPE: Normal
ABILITY: Pickup

264 LINOONE
TYPE: Normal
ABILITY: Pickup

265 WURMPLE
TYPE: Bug
ABILITY: Shield Dust

266 SILCOON
TYPE: Bug
ABILITY: Shed Skin

267 BEAUTIFLY
TYPE: Bug/Flying
ABILITY: Swarm

268 CASCOON
TYPE: Bug
ABILITY: Shed Skin

269 DUSTOX
TYPE: Bug/Poison
ABILITY: Shield Dust

270 LOTAD
TYPE: Water/Grass
ABILITY: Swift Swim/Rain Dish

271 LOMBRE
TYPE: Water/Grass
ABILITY: Swift Swim/Rain Dish

272 LUDICOLO
TYPE: Water/Grass
ABILITY: Swift Swim/Rain Dish

273 SEEDOT
TYPE: Grass
ABILITY: Chlorophyll/Early Bird

274 NUZLEAF
TYPE: Grass/Dark
ABILITY: Chlorophyll/Early Bird

275 SHIFTRY
TYPE: Grass/Dark
ABILITY: Chlorophyll/Early Bird

276 TAILLOW
TYPE: Normal/Flying
ABILITY: Guts

277 SWELLOW
TYPE: Normal/Flying
ABILITY: Guts

278 WINGULL
TYPE: Water/Flying
ABILITY: Keen Eye

279 PELIPPER
TYPE: Water/Flying
ABILITY: Keen Eye

280 RALTS
TYPE: Psychic
ABILITY: Synchronize/Trace

281 KIRLIA
TYPE: Psychic
ABILITY: Synchronize/Trace

282 GARDEVOIR
TYPE: Psychic
ABILITY: Synchronize/Trace

283 SURSKIT
TYPE: Bug/Water
ABILITY: Swift Swim

284 MASQUERAIN
TYPE: Bug/Flying
ABILITY: Intimidate

285 SHROOMISH
TYPE: Grass
ABILITY: Effect Spore

286 BRELOOM
TYPE: Grass/Fighting
ABILITY: Effect Spore

287 SLAKOTH
TYPE: Normal
ABILITY: Truant

288 VIGOROTH
TYPE: Normal
ABILITY: Vital Spirit

Ash's Adventures

Ash Ketchum has had some awesome adventures during his travels across the world of Pokémon. Check out this timeline and follow his journey to become a Pokémon Master.

1 In Pallet Town, Ash has just turned ten years old. He's finally old enough to become a Pokémon Trainer – unfortunately, he oversleeps and misses out on his chance to pick a starter Pokémon! Instead, Professor Oak gives him a Pikachu – an Electric-type Pokémon.

2 Together, Ash and Pikachu begin their journey. Ash and Pikachu leave Pallet Town and set out to win badges from every Gym in the Kanto region. In Ash's travels he gains two companions – Misty and Brock. Ash catches a handful of Pokémon and manages to win a badge from every Gym.

3 Ash eventually makes it to the Pokémon League, where he makes a new friend named Richie – whom he ends up battling. Ash loses and is knocked out of the contest, finishing in the top 16. Ash and his friends are sent on an errand to the Orange Islands to retrieve the mysterious "GS Ball" from Professor Ivy.

7 Cup, where Ash and Misty face off against each other – and Misty wins! Unfortunately, she is defeated in the finals. When Ash has won all of the Johto Gym badges, he registers for the Johto Silver Conference. Ash does really well at the Johto Silver

8 Conference, but in the end he loses. Brock and Misty head home, leaving Ash to journey alone to his next destination – the Hoenn region. Ash heads for the Hoenn region, taking only one of his Pokémon with him – Pikachu. He's joined by May, a new Trainer just starting out on her

9 Pokémon journey, and they pick up two more companions – Brock and May's little brother, Max. May decides to become a Pokémon Coordinator, competing in Pokémon Contests. The four kids travel throughout Hoenn, alternating destinations between Ash's badge battles and May's contests.

#195 QUAGSIRE

Quagsire hunts for food by leaving its mouth wide open in water and waiting for its prey to blunder in unaware. Because the Pokémon does not move, it does not get very hungry.

Type: Water/Ground
Height: 1.4km
Ability: Damp/Water Absorb
Weight: 75kg

#365 WALREIN

Walrein's two massive tusks can shatter icebergs weighing ten tons with one blow. Its thick layer of blubber makes enemy attacks bounce off harmlessly.

Type: Ice/Water
Height: 1.4km
Ability: Thick Fat
Weight: 150.6kg

#253 GROVYLE

The leaves growing out of Grovyle's body camouflage it from enemies in the forest. It is a master at climbing trees in jungles and flying from branch to branch.

Type: Grass
Height: 0.9km
Ability: Overgrow
Weight: 21.6kg

#369 RELICANTH

Relicanth feeds on microscopic organisms. It is a rare species and its body is covered in tough scales like craggy rocks.

Type: Water/Rock
Height: 1.0km
Ability: Swift swim/Rock Head
Weight: 23.4kg

4 When they finally arrive, Brock decides to stay with the professor as her assistant. Ash and Misty travel from island to island. Then Ash decides to compete in the Orange League – and he wins! Ash decides to head

5 to the Johto region – where lots of new Pokémon await. Brock rejoins the group and Ash begins earning badges to enter the Johto League. He catches lots of new Pokémon – but also releases a few of his old Pokémon friends. Ash and his friends continue their journey

6 through the Johto region, where they catch some new Pokémon and meet up with some old human friends from the Kanto region. Ash continues to earn badges – though not every match turns out as easy as he'd like it to be! Ash and friends head for the Whirl Islands to compete in the Whirlpool

10 Ash continues collecting Gym badges while May starts doing much better in Pokémon Contests – winning two ribbons. The two of them capture a few new Pokémon and several of their team also evolve unexpectedly!

11 Ash completes his Hoenn Gym badge collection and May competes in more Pokémon Contests. At last they enter the top competitions for their circuits – the Pokémon League tournament in Ever Grande City and the Pokémon Contest Grand Festival!

TRAINING WRECKS

Ash and his friends had arrived on Muscle Island. They were only one more ferry ride away from Ash's next gym battle!
"There's a ferry from here to Mossdeep City later today," said Brock. They decided to explore the island. But after a long walk they had found nothing at all!
"Anyone else as thirsty as I am?" grumbled May. "You'd think by now we would have found a restaurant or something."
"We haven't even seen any other people yet!" said Brock.
Just then they heard a voice.
"And begin!"
"One, two!" chanted more voices. "One, two! One, two!"
"Hey, what's this?" cried Ash.

Not far away, Team Rocket's submarine surfaced close to Muscle Island. Team Rocket leapt out and raced to shore.

"It's gonna blow!" screamed James. "Run!"

They took cover, but there was no explosion.

"Nothing's happening, Meowth!" said Jessie.

"I never said it was gonna explode," said Meowth.

"James said it was gonna explode!"

Just then the submarine gurgled and sank.

"Noooooo!" screamed Meowth.

"Meowth said we were sinking!" cried James.

"The sub was filling with water!" roared Meowth.

"Because you opened the window!" Jessie and James shouted.

Just then they heard voices.

"One, two!" cried the voices. "One, two! One, two!"

"Huh?" cried Meowth. "What's that?"

In the centre of a clearing, a trainer was instructing a team of body builders.
They were all working out with their Pokémon.
"Looks like some kinda outdoor gym!" said May.
"Do you think they're Pokémon trainers?" asked Max.
"Keep it up, you lightweights, no slacking off!" bellowed the trainer.
He spotted Ash and his friends and walked over to them.
"Hello, my name's Rocky," he said. "I take it you've come here to join my gym?"
"No, we really just showed up by accident," said May.
"We're waiting to catch the ferry to Mossdeep City and we
thought we'd explore the island," said Ash.

"Well, aside from the port, my camp is about all there is to see on Muscle Island," said Rocky.

"Is there a general store?" asked Brock.

"Afraid not," said Rocky.

"We're almost down to the last of our food and water," frowned May.

"Don't worry!" Rocky grinned. "We have enough here to fix something for all of you."

"Wow, are you sure?" asked Brock.

"Yeah!" Rocky replied. "How about if you pay us back with some stories from your travels?"

"What kinda stories?" asked Max.

"Like what different sorts of Pokémon and trainers you've battled," Rocky said. "What kind of strengths and weaknesses they had. We're interested in all that kind of stuff."

"So all of you are Pokémon trainers?" asked Ash.
"That's right," said Rocky. "I run this camp for trainers who wanna get into tip-top shape. How about a little workout before you go? To really master Pokémon battling, building up your physical strength is essential!"
"Count me in, Rocky!" cried Ash. "Let's get started."
"I'll go too!" said Max.
"Why not," said Brock. "I could use a workout."
"How about if I just watch you guys for a while before I make up my mind?" said May.

Team Rocket was hiding in some bushes nearby.

"I just thought of something brilliant," said Meowth. "Why don't we join in? We'll be as strong as them in no time!"

"Meowth, has your brain malfunctioned?" asked Jessie. But James had a strange glow in his eyes.

"Think about it," he said. "We'll get totally pumped up exercising! We'll have muscles on top of muscles! Pikachu will be ours before they know what hit 'em!"

Just then one of the trainers walked up to them.

"Hey there!" he said. "My name's Randy. I bet you're anxious to get your workout started!"

"Yes we are!" grinned James. "Just show us the way!"

Team Rocket was soon working out on running machines.
When Ash and his friends saw them, they were horrified.
"Team Rocket!" Brock gasped.
"We sure do have a lot of guests today," said Rocky.
"Rocky, these three are not the kinda guests that you want at your camp!" Ash warned him.
"They're known as Team Rocket and they're up to no good!" cried Max.
"Well, they haven't done anything wrong since they've arrived here," said Rocky.
"And besides, look how much fun they're having!"
They watched as Team Rocket worked out.
"I guess you're right," said May. "They're not up to anything right now."

"Ash, what's your reason for travelling to Mossdeep City?" asked Rocky.

"I'm going there for a gym battle to try to earn my seventh badge," Ash explained.

"Thought so," grinned Rocky. "How would you like a warm-up battle right now before you go?"

"Rocky's the best trainer here on the island without a doubt," said Randy.

"We're all pretty good but none of us can ever beat him," added one of the girls.

"Let's go for it, Pikachu!" said Ash. "Where should we battle?"

"There's a good spot by the water," said Rocky. He led the way and Ash followed.

"The twerp's gonna battle that muscle-head Rocky!" said Meowth. "All we gotta do is wait until Pikachu's tired out and then we swoop in and grab it!" But Jessie and James weren't listening. They were enjoying the workout!

Down by the shore, Ash and Rocky took their battle positions.
"How about we both pick two Pokémon and have a double battle?" suggested Rocky.
"That sounds good to me!" said Ash.
"Walrein!" called Rocky. "Quagsire! Come on out!"
"Walrein and Quagsire," said Ash as the Pokémon appeared. "Both are Water types. Go get 'em, Pikachu! Grovyle! I choose you!"

"Pikachu, use Thunderbolt on Walrein now!" cried Ash. Quagsire jumped in front of Walrein and took the blast of the attack.
"Quagsire is part Ground-type" Ash realised. "I forgot about that!"

Meanwhile, Brock, May and Max were getting a seriously tough workout!
"Whose bright idea was this anyway?" puffed May.
Team Rocket was finding it tough too.
"I don't care about Pikachu any more," said Jessie. "If I keep running like this there'll be nothing left of me but a skeleton."
"Isn't it wonderful to feel the burn?" exclaimed James. "I love it!"
"This is definitely our worst plan ever!" groaned Meowth.

"Walrein, Ice Ball!" cried Rocky. The Ice Ball hurtled towards Pikachu and Grovyle, but they dodged it just in time.
"Now, use Iron Tail on Walrein – and Grovyle's Leaf Blade on Quagsire!" cried Ash.
But Pikachu and Grovyle collided!
"The key to tag battling is keeping both of your Pokémon synchronised," said Rocky.
"You can't beat me without mastering that!"
Pikachu and Grovyle were hit by another Ice Ball!

"I should have known," sighed Rocky. "I was looking forward to battling an outsider. But I guess you mainland trainers aren't all you're cracked up to be!"
"Don't be so sure, Rocky," said Ash. "I'm still nowhere near beaten!"

"My arms are sore!" groaned Max.
"My back is breaking!" May complained.
They were doing push ups now – and they were in pain!
"My spleen hurts and I don't even know what one is," added Brock.

Team Rocket was still on the running machines. Jessie and Meowth could hardly move, but James was still running.

"I'm so done," said Jessie. "Who cares about Pikachu?"

"Don't quit now!" said James. "You're just starting to build new muscle tissue! Can't you hear your muscles talking to you?"

"Yeah," said Meowth. "They're screaming for help!"

The battle was getting fiercer.
"Grovyle, Bullet Seed attack!" Ash
ordered.
Rocky's Pokémon hid behind some
rocks and the attack missed them.
"Walrein! Another Ice Ball!" yelled
Rocky.
"Strike back with Iron Tail and Leaf
Blade!" Ash cried.
But even though Pikachu and
Grovyle worked together, they
weren't strong enough! The Ice Ball
knocked them down again!
"Walrein's Ice Ball gets more
powerful every time it's launched,"
said Rocky. "The fourth one's
coming up. It'll all be over soon."
    "I wouldn't be so sure about
    that!" Ash yelled.

Max, May and Brock were too tired to carry on with the workout! Max went up to Randy. "We left something really important back on our boat!" he said. "I can get it for you!" said Randy. "That's nice," said Brock, thinking quickly. "But I think it's best if we get it ourselves!" They grabbed their bags and hurried away!

"Hey, that's a good idea!" said Meowth. "Excuse me! We gotta go to our sub! I left the oven on!" "Yes," said Jessie, "and I forgot to water the plants!" "What are you talking about?" cried James. "Our mission depends on this workout!" "No, this workout's over!" yelled Jessie and Meowth.

97

"I gotta think of something," said Ash to himself.
"There has to be a way to stop that attack!
"Ice Ball, Walrein!" yelled Rocky.
Ash watched as the Ice Ball formed. It seemed to take longer to form than the last one.
"The more Ice Balls... the slower they get!" realised Ash. "I've got it!"
"Pikachu, use Thunderbolt on Walrein!" he ordered.
"Guard, Quagsire!" yelled Rocky.
Quagsire jumped in front of Walrein.

"Grovyle, use Leaf Blade on Quagsire!" Ash cried.
Grovyle's attack knocked Quagsire away, so Pikachu could attack Walrein.
"Quick Pikachu, use Thunder on Walrein!" called Ash.
Pikachu's attack hit Walrein full on! Rocky's Pokémon had been beaten!

"That was an incredible comeback!" said Rocky. "You had perfect synchronisation on that combination attack. That was really good!"

"Thanks," said Ash. "But I think you were more impressive!"

"But you won!" Rocky grinned. "Obviously there are some trainers off this Island who are worth battling!"

"Oh yeah, lots!" Ash agreed. "There are tons of trainers out there who are stronger than me!" Just then May, Brock and Max came running up to them.

"Is your battle over already?" asked Max.

"Yep," he replied. "And it was a good one!"

"Yeah!" agreed Rocky. "The best battle I ever lost!"

The ferry sailed away as the sun was setting. Ash and his friends stood on deck.

"We'll wake up in Mossdeep City," said Brock.

"Awesome!" said Ash. "You ready for another great battle, Pikachu?"

Just then, three skippers walked up to Ash.

"Are you this Pikachu's owner?" asked one.

"Yes sir," said Ash. "Why?"

"Don't you know Pokémon are not allowed aboard this ship?" asked another.

Everyone was shocked.

"Just hand over the Pikachu," said the second skipper, grabbing at Pikachu.

"Hey!" yelled Ash. "Get your hands off! What's going on here?"

Jessie, James and Meowth pulled off the skipper disguises!

"Team Rocket!" cried Max. "After our great workout, you twerps won't stand a chance against us!" said James. Jessie threw a net over Pikachu!

Ash and his friends tried to pull the net away from Jessie. James and Meowth hung on to it too. "You'll never out-tug-of-war us!" said Meowth. "Keep the pressure on!" yelled Jessie. "It's starting to come our way!" "Keep pulling, it's coming our way!" cried Brock.

Everyone pulled and pulled. "It's gonna break!" cried Max. Then Pikachu used hit Thunderbolt! Team Rocket blasted off again, and Ash and his friends were safe to continue their journey to Mossdeep City!

289 SLAKING
TYPE: Normal
ABILITY: Truant

290 NINCADA
TYPE: Bug/Ground
ABILITY: Compoundeyes

291 NINJASK
TYPE: Bug/Flying
ABILITY: Speed Boost

292 SHEDINJA
TYPE: Bug/Ghost
ABILITY: Wonder Guard

293 WHISMUR
TYPE: Normal
ABILITY: Soundproof

294 LOUDRED
TYPE: Normal
ABILITY: Soundproof

295 EXPLOUD
TYPE: Normal
ABILITY: Soundproof

296 MAKUHITA
TYPE: Fighting
ABILITY: Thick Fat/Guts

297 HARIYAMA
TYPE: Fighting
ABILITY: Thick Fat/Guts

298 AZURILL
TYPE: Normal
ABILITY: Thick Fat/Huge Power

299 NOSEPASS
TYPE: Rock
ABILITY: Sturdy/Magnet Pull

300 SKITTY
TYPE: Normal
ABILITY: Cute Charm

301 DELCATTY
TYPE: Normal
ABILITY: Cute Charm

302 SABLEYE
TYPE: Dark/Ghost
ABILITY: Keen Eye

303 MAWILE
TYPE: Steel
ABILITY: Hyper Cutter/Intimidate

304 ARON
TYPE: Steel/Rock
ABILITY: Sturdy/Rock Head

305 LAIRON
TYPE: Steel/Rock
ABILITY: Sturdy/Rock Head

306 AGGRON
TYPE: Steel/Rock
ABILITY: Sturdy/Rock Head

307 MEDITITE
TYPE: Fighting/Psychic
ABILITY: Pure Power

308 MEDICHAM
TYPE: Fighting/Psychic
ABILITY: Pure Power

309 ELECTRIKE
TYPE: Electric
ABILITY: Static/Lightningrod

310 MANECTRIC
TYPE: Electric
ABILITY: Static/Lightningrod

311 PLUSLE
TYPE: Electric
ABILITY: Plus

312 MINUN
TYPE: Electric
ABILITY: Minus

313 VOLBEAT
TYPE: Bug
ABILITY: Illuminate/Swarm

314 ILLUMISE
TYPE: Bug
ABILITY: Oblivious

315 ROSELIA
TYPE: Grass/Poison
ABILITY: Natural Cure/Poison Point

316 GULPIN
TYPE: Poison
ABILITY: Liquid Ooze/Sticky Hold

317 SWALOT
TYPE: Poison
ABILITY: Liquid Ooze/Sticky Hold

318 CARVANHA
TYPE: Water/Dark
ABILITY: Rough Skin

319 SHARPEDO
TYPE: Water/Dark
ABILITY: Rough Skin

320 WAILMER
TYPE: Water
ABILITY: Water Veil/Oblivious

321 WAILORD
TYPE: Water
ABILITY: Water Veil/Oblivious

322 NUMEL
TYPE: Fire/Ground
ABILITY: Oblivious

323 CAMERUPT
TYPE: Fire/Ground
ABILITY: Magma Armour

324 TORKOAL
TYPE: Fire
ABILITY: White Smoke

325 SPOINK
TYPE: Psychic
ABILITY: Thick Fat/Own Tempo

326 GRUMPIG
TYPE: Psychic
ABILITY: Thick Fat/Own Tempo

327 SPINDA
TYPE: Normal
ABILITY: Own Tempo

328 TRAPINCH
TYPE: Ground
ABILITY: Hyper Cutter/Arena Trap

329 VIBRAVA
TYPE: Ground/Dragon
ABILITY: Levitate

330 FLYGON
TYPE: Ground/Dragon
ABILITY: Levitate

331 CACNEA
TYPE: Grass
ABILITY: Sand Veil

332 CACTURNE
TYPE: Grass/Dark
ABILITY: Sand Veil

333 SWABLU
TYPE: Normal/Flying
ABILITY: Natural Cure

334 ALTARIA
TYPE: Dragon/Flying
ABILITY: Natural Cure

335 ZANGOOSE
TYPE: Normal
ABILITY: Immunity

336 SEVIPER
TYPE: Poison
ABILITY: Shed Skin

337 LUNATONE
TYPE: Rock/Psychic
ABILITY: Levitate

338 SOLROCK
TYPE: Rock/Psychic
ABILITY: Levitate

339 BARBOACH
TYPE: Water/Ground
ABILITY: Oblivious

340 WHISCASH
TYPE: Water/Ground
ABILITY: Oblivious

341 CORPHISH
TYPE: Water
ABILITY: Hyper Cutter/Shell Armour

342 CRAWDAUNT
TYPE: Water/Dark
ABILITY: Hyper Cutter/Shell Armour

343 BALTOY
TYPE: Ground/Psychic
ABILITY: Levitate

344 CLAYDOL
TYPE: Ground/Psychic
ABILITY: Levitate

345 LILEEP
TYPE: Rock/Grass
ABILITY: Suction Cups

346 CRADILY
TYPE: Rock/Grass
ABILITY: Suction Cups

347 ANORITH
TYPE: Rock/Bug
ABILITY: Battle Armour

348 ARMALDO
TYPE: Rock/Bug
ABILITY: Battle Armour

349 FEEBAS
TYPE: Water
ABILITY: Swift Swim

350 MILOTIC
TYPE: Water
ABILITY: Marvel Scale

351 CASTFORM
TYPE: Normal
ABILITY: Forecast

352 KECLEON
TYPE: Normal
ABILITY: Colour Change

353 SHUPPET
TYPE: Ghost
ABILITY: Insomnia

354 BANETTE
TYPE: Ghost
ABILITY: Insomnia

355 DUSKULL
TYPE: Ghost
ABILITY: Levitate

356 DUSCLOPS
TYPE: Ghost
ABILITY: Pressure

357 TROPIUS
TYPE: Grass/Flying
ABILITY: Chlorophyll

358 CHIMECHO
TYPE: Psychic
ABILITY: .Levitate

359 ABSOL
TYPE: Dark
ABILITY: Pressure

360 WYNAUT
TYPE: Psychic
ABILITY: Shadow Tag

361 SNORUNT
TYPE: Ice
ABILITY: Inner Focus

362 GLALIE
TYPE: Ice
ABILITY: Inner Focus

363 SPHEAL
TYPE: Ice/Water
ABILITY: Thick Fat

364 SEALEO
TYPE: Ice/Water
ABILITY: Thick Fat

365 WALREIN
TYPE: Ice/Water
ABILITY: Thick Fat

366 CLAMPERL
TYPE: Water
ABILITY: Shell Armour

367 HUNTAIL
TYPE: Water
ABILITY: Swift Swim

368 GOREBYSS
TYPE: Water
ABILITY: Swift Swim

369 RELICANTH
TYPE: Water/Rock
ABILITY: Swift Swim/Rock Head

370 LUVDISC
TYPE: Water
ABILITY: Swift Swim

371 BAGON
TYPE: Dragon
ABILITY: Rock Head

372 SHELGON
TYPE: Dragon
ABILITY: Rock Head

373 SALAMENCE
TYPE: Dragon/Flying
ABILITY: Intimidate

374 BELDUM
TYPE: Steel/Psychic
ABILITY: Clear Body

375 METANG
TYPE: Steel/Psychic
ABILITY: Clear Body

376 METAGROSS
TYPE: Steel/Psychic
ABILITY: Clear Body

377 REGIROCK
TYPE: Rock
ABILITY: Clear Body

378 REGICE
TYPE: Ice
ABILITY: Clear Body

379 REGISTEEL
TYPE: Steel
ABILITY: Clear Body

380 LATIAS
TYPE: Dragon/Psychic
ABILITY: Levitate

381 LATIOS
TYPE: Dragon/Psychic
ABILITY: Levitate

382 KYOGRE
TYPE: Water
ABILITY: Drizzle

383 GROUDON
TYPE: Ground
ABILITY: Drought

384 RAYQUAZA
TYPE: Dragon/Flying
ABILITY: Air Lock

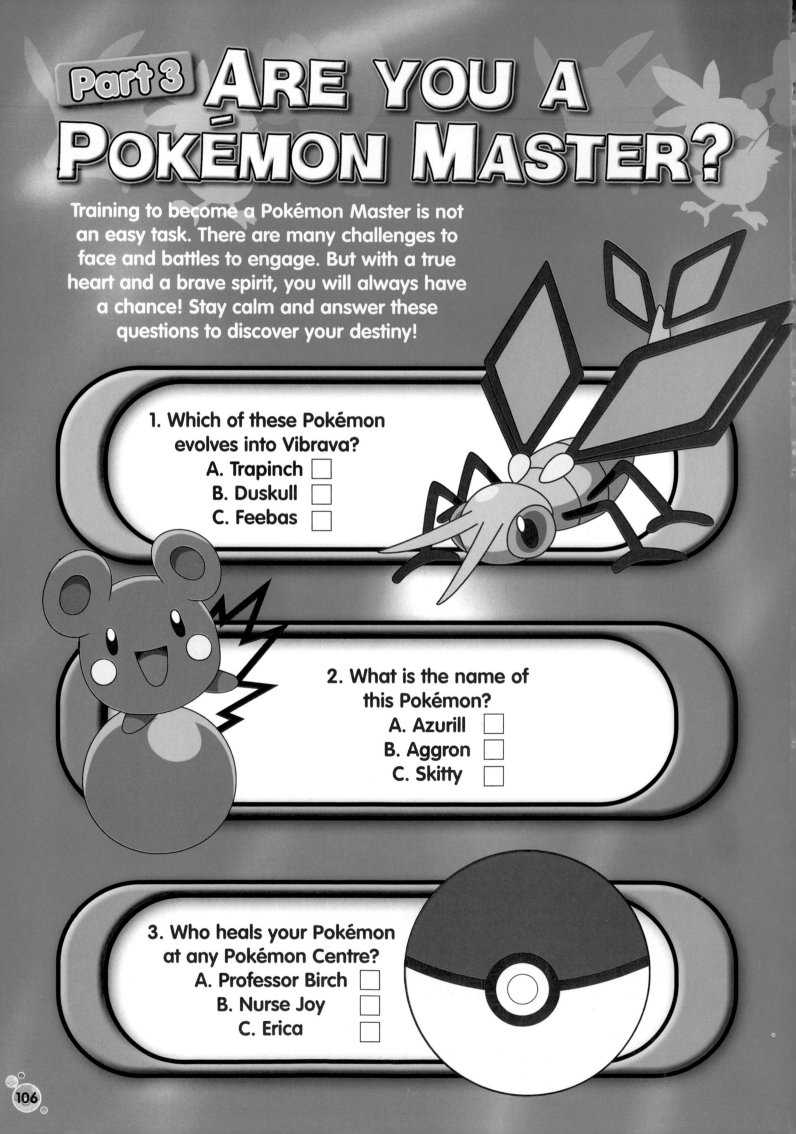

Part 3 ARE YOU A POKÉMON MASTER?

Training to become a Pokémon Master is not an easy task. There are many challenges to face and battles to engage. But with a true heart and a brave spirit, you will always have a chance! Stay calm and answer these questions to discover your destiny!

1. Which of these Pokémon evolves into Vibrava?
   A. Trapinch ☐
   B. Duskull ☐
   C. Feebas ☐

2. What is the name of this Pokémon?
   A. Azurill ☐
   B. Aggron ☐
   C. Skitty ☐

3. Who heals your Pokémon at any Pokémon Centre?
   A. Professor Birch ☐
   B. Nurse Joy ☐
   C. Erica ☐

4. Which of these Pokémon has toxic spores?
A. Shroomish ☐
B. Absol ☐
C. Wynaut ☐

5. Which was the first league Ash entered?
A. Hoenn League ☐
B. Indigo League ☐
C. Orange League ☐

6. What do Pikachu's cheek pouches store?
A. Pokéblock ☐
B. Water ☐
C. Electricity ☐

ANSWERS: 1.Trapinch 2.Azurill 3.Nurse Joy 4.Shroomish 5.Indigo League 6.Electricity

Now add this result to your others to get a final score. How many did you get right?

18 – Awesome! You're a true Pokémon master! Ash would be glad of your help on his adventures. But remember, there is always more to learn about Pokémon!

13-17 – You're almost there! You have learnt a great deal, but you are not quite focused enough. Keep training and you'll soon be a Pokémon master.

7-12 – You've got a long way to go – pay more attention to your Pokémon. You will never be a Pokémon master unless you spend time and energy on your studies.

1-6 – You're not trying very hard. Are you *sure* you want to be a Pokémon trainer? If you want to be like Ash, you've gotta put the work in!

Fill in the Missing Evolutions

Team Rocket has caused a terrible mess at the Pokémon Centre! All Nurse Joy's papers are muddled up. Can you help her out by filling in the missing evolutions?

TRAPINCH
EVOLVES INTO
V I _ _ R _ a

RALTS
EVOLVES INTO
K _ r L _ a

SHELGON
EVOLVES INTO
S _ _ _ M _ C _

ANORITH
EVOLVES INTO
_ _ r _ a L D _

METANG
EVOLVES INTO
_ _ _ _ _ _ G r

BULBASAUR
EVOLVES INTO
I _ Y _ S _ _ r

ZIGZAGOON
EVOLVES INTO
L _ N O _ N _

WYNAUT
EVOLVES INTO
WO _ B _ FF _ _

TREECKO
EVOLVES INTO
G _ _ VYL _

MUST-HAVE TOOLS FOR TOP TRAINERS!

The Poké Ball

Pokémon are caught when a Poké Ball is thrown towards them. A modern Poké Ball opens when it is thrown and quickly draws the Pokémon inside. Pokémon that are caught in this way become instantly loyal to their Trainers.

Trainers use a Poké Ball to carry their Pokémon around as they go on their journeys. Most Trainers let their Pokémon rest in their Poké Ball between battles and feedings.

When a Poké Ball is not in use, it shrinks down so that it can be easily stored in a backpack or on a belt. This device comes in many different varieties, and each has its uses.

The PokéNav

The PokéNav is only found in the Hoenn region. It contains information on Trainers, detailed data about various Pokémon and maps of the region.

The Pokédex

The Pokédex is an electronic index with information on all the known species of Pokémon. This is very useful to Trainers, especially when their opponent uses a Pokémon they haven't battled before. With help from the Pokédex, Trainers can choose the right Pokémon to battle with.

#385 JIRACHI

Jirachi is said to grant any wish that people desire. If this Pokémon senses danger, it will fight without awakening.

Type: ?????????? **Ability:** ?????????
Height: 0.3km **Weight:** 1.1kg

#386 DEOXYS

Deoxys emerged from a virus that came from space. There is a crystalline organ on its chest, which seems to be its brain.

Type: ?????????? **Ability:** ?????????
Height: 1.7km **Weight:** 60.8kg

S	U	D	W	D	H	F	P	Y	T	H	A	R	A	T
K	F	H	V	X	E	Y	S	J	P	O	E	G	S	V
P	S	E	R	T	L	O	M	N	I	D	R	P	H	E
O	P	U	J	Y	F	E	A	D	N	I	L	H	S	W
A	N	C	F	J	S	U	K	A	T	E	Q	D	A	A
K	E	H	D	F	E	I	M	B	J	R	H	O	D	R
J	C	N	I	Y	L	R	O	T	L	G	X	A	I	O
W	N	Q	B	L	A	Z	I	K	E	N	I	F	P	K
A	O	S	S	H	T	S	R	H	K	D	P	H	A	L
S	E	A	C	R	E	Y	W	A	T	G	L	J	R	I
L	R	G	F	V	N	A	V	A	L	I	U	Q	D	A
U	A	W	P	U	I	C	B	T	R	K	V	S	F	L
G	L	A	U	R	N	V	L	F	S	Y	T	I	O	P
M	F	I	S	J	T	I	O	X	P	O	N	Y	T	A
A	Z	R	Q	K	M	C	S	R	E	B	I	U	T	B

WORDSEARCH ANSWERS